Jesus Then and Now WORKBOOK

Based on the book by
David Watson and Simon Jenkins
and the video produced by
Lella Productions

Study material by Mags Law

LION PUBLISHING
with
LELLA PRODUCTIONS

Copyright © 1983 Lion Publishing
Published by
Lion Publishing plc
Icknield Way, Tring, Herts, England
ISBN 0 85648 522 7

Albatross Books
PO Box 320, Sutherland, NSW 2232, Australia
ISBN 0 86760 390 9

First edition 1983 in association with Lella Productions

INTRODUCTION

This workbook is designed for use with the book *Jesus Then and Now,* by David Watson and Simon Jenkins, Lion 1983, or with the video of the same title, produced by Lella Productions.

The questions and discussion ideas have been written:
● to help you to absorb and evaluate what you have read in the book or seen on the video;
● to help you to see for yourself what the Bible has to say about Jesus, and how what he said and did can relate to our lives today. This material can be used individually or by groups working together.

Using the Bible
It is vital to understand what the Gospels say, and not just work out our own ideas. So in each section references to passages or verses in the Bible are given. It does not matter which translation you use. There are several modern English versions, of which I would recommend the Good News Bible and the New International Version as the most readable and comprehensible.

When the reader is pointed to a passage or 'reference' in the Bible, it is given as follows: Matthew 13:44-46, which simply means Matthew's Gospel, chapter 13, verses 44 to 46.

Where single verses are given, it is usually helpful to read the verses just before and following that verse, so that you can see the situation or context in which the words were written or spoken.

After some of the questions, several references are given. It is usually not necessary to look up all these verses; one or two are often sufficient. The additional ones are given for those working in groups, or for those who are particularly interested in finding out more about that issue. The two main references are printed in bold type.

Some longer passages from the Bible, on which a whole section is based, are given under the heading 'read it yourself'. It is *not* necessary to read all these passages before you work through the section; they are there so that you know where to find them should you need to refer to them.

Using the video

If you are leading a small group using the video series of *Jesus Then and Now,* you should note the following points:

● View each programme and read the relevant section of the notes beforehand. Decide which areas your group would benefit from discussing.

● At the beginning of the video tape, set the counter on your video recorder to zero. Note the footage numbers for the start of any sequences you may wish to replay during the course of group study so that valuable time is not lost in searching the tape.

● Remember that video is not like live television. You can stop, go back, and take the programme at the pace best suited for your group. Occasionally the screen fades to black in some programmes, and these are designed as ideal points to stop the tape for thought or discussion.

Are there 'right' and 'wrong' answers?

Quite simply, this depends on the question! When you are answering the questions, it often helps to think them through in three stages: What do I think? What do I think the Bible says? What do other Christians say?

Often it is helpful to write down your answers to the questions and there are some pages at the back of the workbook which you can use for this.

Thought for action

Jesus' words and life demand a response from us − both a personal response to him, and a response in our actions. Many of the sections therefore include a suggestion for action. Don't limit yourself to these ideas; they are a jumping-off point rather than an end in themselves.

Jesus Then and Now, or Jesus Now and Then?

I hope that you will find the questions in this workbook both interesting and thought-provoking. While I was working on them, I once or twice made the mistake of referring to the book as 'Jesus Now and Then'! Perhaps that is what is lacking in our discipleship nowadays − we tend to include Jesus in our lives only 'now and then'. I hope that working through this book will help to make our discipleship a more continuous experience and our friendship with Jesus a more integral part of our lives.

Mags Law

1 BEGINNINGS

Why look at Jesus?

1 If someone asked you, 'Why should I bother to think about Jesus?' what reasons would you give them?

2 What made *you* decide to look at Jesus?
If you are working in a group, compare the reasons each of you would give for thinking about Jesus.

3 Have a look at what different people in the first century thought of Jesus and his influence. You will find some very different views in these verses: **John 6:66-69**; John 7:12; John 11:25-27; **Acts 5:27-40**; Acts 17:5-7; Acts 19:23-27.

4 Looking back from the twentieth century, what do you think of these reactions? Do people still react to Jesus in the same way?

How can we know about Jesus?

5 Why did the Gospel writers write their accounts of Jesus' life?
Mark is brief and to the point:
'This is the Good News about Jesus Christ, the Son of God.' Mark 1:1.
  Luke and John are more explicit. Read Luke 1:1-4, and John 20:30-31 and 21:24.

Why are there four different accounts?
6 Each of the four Gospels gives us a different view of the events of Jesus' life. This exercise will take you a little time, but it is well worth it.
  Look at the story of the feeding of five thousand people. The four different accounts are in Matthew 14:13-21; Mark 6:30-44; Luke 9:10-17; John 6:1-14.
  If you are looking at this in a group, ask four people to take the role of the four authors. Read the accounts out loud, in turn, and ask the 'authors' to point out the things they remembered, which are not in the other accounts. For example, John might say, 'I remember Jesus told us to collect up what was left so that it wouldn't be wasted.' (Only John's account records Jesus telling the disciples to do this.)
  You can look at the accounts of Jesus' arrest in a similar way. The verses in brackets show some of the 'extra' details, which reflect the particular author's view of the events. Jesus' arrest is recorded in Matthew 26:47-56 (verses 53, 54, 56); Mark 14:43-52 (verses 51, 52); Luke 22:47-53 (verse 51); John 18:1-11 (verses 9, 10, 11).

For further discussion

7 Do you think the Gospel writers could have invented the story of
Jesus' life? Do you think they *would* have done, bearing in mind all
Jesus' teaching?

Into what kind of world was Jesus born?

(Omit this section if time is short.)

8 What were the main hopes and feelings of each of the different
religious and political groups at the time of Jesus? *(Jesus Then and
Now,* pages 14-19.)

9 From what you already know of Jesus, what in his teaching would
have disappointed — and excited — each of these groups?

What do you think?

10 Does understanding the political, religious and geographical situation
during Jesus' lifetime give us a better understanding of his teaching?
If so, think of one particular way this knowledge is a help.

Why was Jesus' birth different?

Read it for yourself

11 Read Matthew 1:18-25 and Luke 1:5 — 2:40 and see how Jesus' birth
was different:
- *different* in the way it came about (Jesus was not conceived
through a normal, human sexual relationship);
- *different* in the special events surrounding it;
- *different* in its meaning.

Dig a bit deeper

12 Look at some of these verses, and see the meaning that the New
Testament writers saw in the birth and life of Jesus: Colossians
1:15-20; Philippians 2:6-8; Hebrews 1:1-3; Hebrews 4:14, 15;
John 1:14; Luke 2:25-35.

Think it over

13 Re-read the story of the birth of Jesus and, choosing one character,
spend a few minutes trying to understand that person's feelings about
what was happening.

For further reading
The New Testament Documents F. F. Bruce (IVP).
Christianity: the witness of history J. N. D. Anderson (IVP).

2 TEMPTATION

Who was John the Baptist?

Read it for yourself
The birth of John: Luke 1:5-25, 57-80
John's preaching: **Luke 3:1-20;** John 1:19-37; Matthew 3:1-12;
Mark 1:1-8.
1 What were the two main points of John's message?
2 What was John's practical teaching about the kingdom?

Jesus and the kingdom
3 Look at some of Jesus' teaching about the kingdom of God.
Remember that the Jewish people were hoping for a king to deliver
them from the Romans. Jesus plainly had a different kind of
kingdom in mind: Mark 1:15; Matthew 21:28-32; **Matthew 18:21-35;**
Matthew 13:44-50; Luke 14:15-24; John 18:33-38.
   Christians are to echo Jesus' prayer, 'May your kingdom come'.
So how does Jesus' teaching in these verses apply to our lives today?
4 Look at how working to bring God's rule into effect in the world
affected the lives of:
● Jesus: Matthew 3:13-15; Matthew 26:39, 42
● Mary: Luke 1:38
● Peter: Acts 4:18, 19; Acts 5:27-29
Does acknowledging Jesus' kingship in our lives affect us in the same
sort of way?

Repentance
5 Some Jews felt they had no need to repent because they were relying
on the fact that they were the chosen people. Matthew 3:7-9
What reasons do people give nowadays for saying they are not wrong
in God's sight?
6 Read Luke 5:30-32; Luke 6:41, 42
What do you think Jesus meant when he said these things?

Practical Repentance
7 Read Luke 19:1-9.
Do you agree with Graham Turner that for repentance to mean
anything it must involve positive action? (Replay the video or see
page 25 of the book).
   Are there some situations where to try to put things right would
cause more harm?
8 Think of Graham's situation and the four things he felt he had to
put right. What sort of arguments might he (or his friends) have put
up for simply stopping doing those things, but without trying to put
right the past?

Why did Jesus leave Nazareth?

9 What did baptism symbolize for John and his followers? Luke 3:3;
Mark 1:4, 5

10 Now look at what Peter and Paul taught about baptism.
Acts 2:38, 39; Romans 6:4; 1 Corinthians 12:13; Colossians 2:12
What does Christian baptism represent?

Does the devil really exist?

11 Before you work through this section, stop and think, 'Do I believe
that the devil exists as a personal being?' If you do, is it because:
● the Bible teaches that he exists?
● I know from my own experience?
● Jesus believed in his existence?
● I believe it from looking at the world around me?
● Some other reason?
If you are working in a group, you could compare your reasons.
Most people find it more difficult to believe in a personal devil that
in some vague evil force. Why do you think this is?

12 What do you think is the wisest attitude for a Christian to take to
the occult today?
● Ignore it?
● Keep informed so that you know what you are up against?
● Keep well away from anything to do with it?

What do Jesus' temptations teach us?

Read it for yourself
Matthew 4:1-11; Mark 1:12-13; Luke 4:1-13

13 In each of the temptations, the devil took some part of Jesus'
ministry which was good, and tried to get Jesus to use this power in
the wrong way. How do you think we can guard against being
diverted in a similar way, and using our gifts and talents wrongly?

Jesus and us

14 Does it help to memorize verses from the Bible?

15 Look at Matthew 26:36-38.
Jesus prayed, and wanted the support and companionship of his
disciples. When we face temptation, do we pray, and are there
Christians whom we feel we can ask for support?

16 Read Luke 22:31, 32; 1 Corinthians 10:13; Hebrews 7:35.
How are these verses an encouragement to us when we face
temptation?

3 DISCIPLES

Why did Jesus call the disciples?

Read it for yourself
Jesus calls the disciples Matthew 4:18-22; Matthew 9:9;
Mark 1:14-20; John 1:35-49

Quick facts to check on the disciples
1 Why did Jesus call the disciples? Mark 3:14, 15
2 Were their backgrounds similar or different? Mark 1:14-20; 2:13, 14
3 How did Jesus promise to help his disciples when he was no longer
  with them? Matthew 28:20; Luke 21:14, 15; John 14:16, 17;
  Acts 1:3-5, 8
     What did Jesus want from, and for, his disciples? Luke 9:23, 24;
  Mark 3:31-35; Luke 21:34-36; John 17:6-26

Think it over
4 If we are disciples of Jesus, we can take what Jesus said and apply it
  to our lives. Do we see Jesus' commands, and his prayer, coming
  true in us?
5 The disciples gave up their jobs to follow Jesus. Did we give up
  anything specific to follow him? Should we have done? If you have
  used the video, think back to and discuss the drama sequence in
  which the disciples argued over what the call of Jesus may have
  meant for them.
6 When we doubt God's presence with us, or do not understand what
  is happening in our lives, it can often help to see the disciples doubts
  and fears. Look at one or two of these passages and see how Jesus
  both understood and answered the disciples need: John 14:1-14;
  Matthew 14:22-33; John 20:24-29

What does discipleship mean?

7 Try for a moment to put yourself in the place of someone, not a
  Christian, who knows you. Ask yourself, 'Does . . . know I'm a
  Christian?' Suggest to each other (or to yourself) some of the ways in
  which your friend might know you follow Jesus. (Be honest!)
8 Generally speaking, what sort of things do people who are not
  Christians use to identify a Christian? Do any of these phrases sound
  familiar?
  'He's religious . . . She goes to church . . . He doesn't swear . . .
  She believes in the Bible and all that . . . He doesn't drink . . . He
  hasn't got much sense of humour' (this sometimes, but not always,
  means 'He doesn't laugh at dirty jokes') . . . 'She prays to God . . .
  He doesn't fiddle the expenses . . . She's always talking about God.'

Now compare these statements with what Jesus said about being a disciple: Luke 14:25, 26; **Matthew 25:37-40;** John 14:23, 24, 27; **John 13:34, 35; John 15:11;** John 17:21-23
(For more of Jesus' teaching, look at Luke 6:27-38)

It's too difficult
9 Even when people see in us the qualities that Jesus said we should show, there will still be opposition. What do Jesus' example and teaching tell us about how we should react to unwarranted criticism and opposition? **Luke 12:4-7, 11, 12;** Matthew 5:10-12; **John 16:33;** John 17:14, 15

10 One of the twelve apostles, Peter, wrote in his letter to some fellow-Christians about the suffering that disciples of Jesus must be prepared to face. You can read what he wrote in 1 Peter 2:21-23 and 1 Peter 4:12-16. Notice that Jesus and Peter are talking all the time about opposition that comes as a result of following Jesus. Are there some sorts of opposition and suffering that we bring on ourselves? (See also Margaret Dehqani-Tafti on the video or on page 50 of the book.)

Sometimes it seems that the hardest part of discipleship is living with other disciples! Even Jesus' close friends didn't always get on with each other. Read Mark 10:35-45 and Mark 9:33-37. We are often so sure we are right! Jesus' first disciples were just the same. Look at Mark 10:13-15 and Matthew 16:21-23. It's worth remembering these incidents next time we are sure we know best.

What effect does discipleship have?
Salt and Light
11 Jesus said his disciples (that's you and me!):'**You** are the light of the world . . . **you** are the salt of the earth.' (Delia Smith explains some uses of salt on the video.) Can you think of at least one way in which your life as a disciple of Jesus can be salt . . . and light:
● in your home?
● in your place of work, or school?
● in your leisure activities?

Making disciples
12 Read these verses first: 1 Thessalonians 5:14; 2 Timothy 2:2. Discuss with others (or think over yourself) the four steps in discipling suggested in *Jesus Then and Now,* page 49.
    In what areas of your Christian life do you think these steps could help you?

13 Do you agree with the four steps suggested? Are they put into practice in your local group of Christians? If not, how could they be?

14 Are there any principles about working with others that we can learn from the way Jesus sent out his disciples? Look at Mark 6:7-13 and Luke 10:1-12.

4 MIRACLES

Why is there pain and suffering?

Read it for yourself

1 God made a plan: **Genesis 1:26-31**; Psalm 8:1-9; Psalm 115:15-16
but mankind rebelled: **Genesis 3:6-13;**Isaiah 53:6; Romans 1:20-23
This rebellion has spoiled relationships: **Genesis 4:1-10**; James 4:1;
Amos 5:10-12
and deeply marred our world: **Genesis 3:17-19**; Isaiah 24:4, 5
Did Jesus promise that his followers would be spared suffering?
Look at Mark 13:5-13, and see Godfrey Williams on the video or
page 62 of the book.

2 The writer of Psalm 73 knew what it was to suffer without knowing
the reason:

> When my thoughts were bitter
> and my feelings were hurt,
> I was as stupid as an animal,
> I did not understand you.
> Yet I always stay close to you,
> and you hold me by the hand.
> You guide me with your instruction
> and at the end you will receive me with honour.
> What else have I in heaven but you?
> Since I have you, what else could I want on earth?
> My mind and my body may grow weak, but God is my strength;
> he is all I ever need.   *Psalm 73:21-26*

Read the rest of the psalm for yourself. What emotions does the
writer feel? What are the things that encourage him?

Act it out

3 If you are working in a group, one or two members could take the
role of people who are not Christians, and challenge the rest of the
group with these questions:
Why do the innocent suffer, if God is a God of love?
Why does God allow suffering? Can't he stop it?
Why don't Christians do more to stop suffering? All they do is
preach about accepting it bravely!
    The two people taking on the questioning role need to be ruthless
and not accept terms or explanations they don't understand.

Prayer and action

4 Pray that God will show you a practical way in which you can help
to relieve the suffering of some in your immediate community, and in
other parts of the world — and then do something about it.

Why did Jesus work miracles?

A quick language lesson!
The English word 'miracle' is used for three different words in Greek (the language the Gospels were written in):
- 'mighty works' – effectiveness, or power;
- 'wonders';
- 'signs', with deep significance.

5 In our 'scientific' age most people think that miracles are above (or even against) the natural laws of the universe, as if, in miracles, God is 'interfering' with the natural order. At the back of our minds we often make the mistake of thinking of God as setting the universe to work like a piece of machinery. But the Bible always shows God in a living and personal relationship with his creation.

Discuss with each other what you think about miracles. Do you believe they happen? What is happening when a miracle occurs? What part does faith play?

6 Some people today try to 'explain away' what Christians would call miracles by saying 'it's all psychological' (as with healing, for example) or 'it's just coincidence'. What would be your response to this?

The miracles of Jesus
Look at one or two of the miracles Jesus performed, as in Luke 5:18-26 or Luke 13:10-17. See if you can answer these questions:

7 Why did Jesus work this miracle?
8 Was it easy for Jesus to work miracles?

Do the miracles prove who Jesus was?

9 Look again at the miracle stories in Luke. What was the effect of this miracle on the people there at the time?
10 In what way was this miracle significant – a sign pointing to who Jesus was?
11 Did the miracles prove to people who Jesus was?

Find it hard to believe?
If you find the question of miracles difficult, it's well worth doing a bit of homework. For example look at the entry on 'Miracles' in *The Lion Handbook of Christian Belief*.

Miracles today?

12 If someone who is ill were to ask you, 'Should I ask God to heal me?', what would you say?

5 LIFESTYLE

How did Jesus live?

Look at Luke 9:57-62
1 Jesus gave up a secure, well-paid job for an uncertain, dangerous life. Does this mean we should do the same?
2 Jesus depended on the hospitality and support of his sympathizers. Are all his followers called to do this? See Luke 8:3 and Ephesians 4:28.
3 We have seen that Jesus and many of his followers sacrificed their financial security, even their social popularity. How important to you is:
- financial security?
- social acceptance?
4 Some Christians lose one or both of these through, for example, unemployment, not necessarily as a direct result of following Jesus. How hard would you find it to cope with losing these two things? Do you think you would feel differently, depending on what caused the loss?
5 Jesus knew no 'us' and 'them' (look at Luke 7:36-39). His disciples had to learn the same lesson (Acts 10:19-35, 45). In what practical ways can we follow this example of Jesus today?
6 In *Jesus Then and Now* (page 68) Jean Vanier says, 'I think the most important thing is for us all to say . . . "How can I, today, at my home, in my little community life, my family life, become open to a rejected person?" '
   Think about this for a few moments in practical terms. For example: Should Christians be more prepared to be foster parents? What about our attitude to, and involvement with, mentally handicapped people? . . . those in prison? . . . prostitutes? What about our reaction to those at school, or work, who are unpopular?

What did Jesus teach about lifestyle?

Inner Change
7 Read these verses: **Mark 7:14-23; Matthew 23:25-28;** Luke 16:15; 1 Samuel 16:6, 7
   Ask yourselves, 'What inner changes has God made in me? What outward effect have these changes had?'
8 What other changes do you think God wants to bring about in you?

How should we live?

9 What do you think the main pressures of our consumer society are?
10 Replay the video of Ronald Sider or read the section 'Christian

Action for the Poor' (page 76 in *Jesus Then and Now*). Do you agree with what Ronald Sider says?

11 Do you think his suggestions could work, in practical terms?

12 Which of the suggestions, if any, do you think could be tried in your local fellowship, or among a smaller group of local Christians?

13 Read Jesus' words in Luke 14:12-14. Whose home was Jesus eating at? (Look back to verse 1 of the chapter.)

14 Should we take what Jesus says here literally, next time we hold a party? If not, why not? (If you think this is one isolated saying, look at Luke 6:32-38.)

15 Does what Jesus says make us uncomfortable?

16 Did he really mean us to do what he says?

Take up the challenge

17 *As a group.* Decide on one positive change you could make in your life style (either as individuals or through group action) to reflect Jesus' teaching more closely. Think about the practical details, the possible snags, and the commitment needed. Then **do it** – don't just talk about it!

18 *Individually.* Think through what you have learnt about Christian lifestyle and see if there is a particular attitude you hold which you feel God wants to change. Make changing this attitude a point to think, pray and act on over the next few weeks.

Words to remember

'Instead (of worrying about food and clothes) . . . be concerned above everthing else with the kingdom of God and with what he requires of you, and he will provide you with all these other things.'
Matthew 6:33

6 PRAYER

What is Prayer?

Think It Over

1 How would you answer someone who said that prayer is just a psychological trick?

2 What did Jesus teach his disciples to call God? Look at Luke 11:1, 2.

Prayer is a relationship with God our Father

3 Think of your closest friend and the relationship you have with him or her. Ask yourself:
- What do I give to the relationship?
- What do I receive from the relationship?
- What makes this friendship a good one?

(It may help you to think more clearly if you write down some ideas.)

Now take your answers one at a time and ask:

Do I see these things in my relationship with God?

If not, how can prayer help me to begin to develop them?

4 If you are studying this book in a group, ask each person what he or she finds to be the most important thing about prayer, and which aspect of prayer is the most difficult. Share some of the things which each person has found a help in praying, and some of the ways that prayers have been answered.

What can Jesus teach us about prayer?

5 'Christians believe that prayer changes people and events, and not only the one who prays.' (*Jesus Then and Now,* page 82) Look again at the occasions when Jesus prayed. If we followed Jesus' example for each of these occasions, how might prayer both help us **and** change events?
- Early in the morning Mark 1:35
- Before big decisions Luke 6:12, 13
- Facing temptation, and situations difficult to understand Matthew 26:36-41
- Needing encouragement or strength Luke 3:21, 22; Luke 5:16
- Concern for others Luke 22:31, 32; John 17:20, 21

Read the section 'There are no rules in prayer' on page 88 of the book, and discuss.

Why is prayer so difficult?

6 Ask yourself why, and when, you find prayer most difficult.

Do any of these reasons sound familiar?
- When I feel it to be a duty.

- When I know I haven't obeyed God.
- I don't feel the need to pray.
- When I haven't prayed much recently.
- When my prayers don't seem to be answered.

Do you have other reasons?

How can we solve these kinds of difficulty?

7 If we see prayer as part of our relationship with God, should we expect it always to be easy?

How can we develop in prayer?

8 David Watson and Simon Jenkins suggest six things that will help us to develop in prayer. (*Jesus Then and Now*, pages 92-96)

Each of these six things could be applied to building any friendship. We could spend a long time studying Jesus' approach to prayer, or discussing the subject of prayer with others, neither of them good substitutes for getting on with praying and building our friendship with God. So, taking each of the six suggestions, write down a way of putting each into practical effect in your life. Take another look at your notes in a week's time and see if you have started doing these things.

An example would be: Sometimes when you are talking to a friend, remember that Jesus is in on the conversation. If there is an empty seat, think of it as where he is sitting.

Replay the video (or read page 93 of the book); where Metropolitan Anthony of Sourozh speaks on prayer. He stresses the need to prepare ourselves for prayer. Do we tend to approach God without realizing who he is?

More about prayer
Luke 18:1-14; Matthew 6:5-15; Luke 11:1-13; Romans 8:26, 27; James 5:13-18; Hebrews 4:15, 16; Colossians 4:2-4

Further reading
Prayer is for You, by Graham Claydon (available from ISCF, 130 City Road, London, EC1V 2NJ, 40p).

7 THE MAN

What kind of person was Jesus?

The wrong people

1 Why was it so shocking to the Jews to see Jesus eating with tax collectors?

2 What other people did Jesus mix with? Look at **Luke 7:1-9, 31-35; Luke 8:1-3, 40, 42;** Luke 5:12, 13; Luke 14:1

3 With whom do you think Jesus would be spending his time, if he was living in your town today?

4 Why was Jesus prepared to break the social rules of his time? Read Luke 5:30-32; Mark 6:34

5 From reading some of the following verses, what sort of things do you think made Jesus angry or sad? **John 2:13-17; Luke 11:46, 52; John 11:32-36;** John 13:21

6 What sort of things should Christians be angry about today? Do you think they should be more concerned with social injustice than with individual sin?

7 Spend a few moments thinking quietly about whether there is anything in the way you live which would sadden or anger Jesus.

8 'When we listen to what Jesus said about himself, we hear things that no one in his right mind would dream of saying unless they were true.' (*Jesus Then and Now,* page 108)
Look again at some of the things Jesus said: **Luke 5:20-26; John 10: 25-33;** John 11:25, 26; Mark 14: 61-64; Luke 22:19, 20
What would be your reaction if someone you knew said things like this to you? What were people's reactions at the time?

9 Peter knew Jesus better than anyone. What did he think?
'Jesus is the one of whom the scripture says, "The stone that you despised turned out to be the most important of all." Salvation is to be found through him alone; in all the world there is no one else whom God has given who can save us.' Acts 4:11, 12. See also Acts 2:22-24 and 1 Peter 2:22. So we see that Jesus' life backed up what he said about himself.

Who did Jesus say he was?

10 Look again at 'Jesus tells us who he is' (page 105 in *Jesus Then and Now*). Ask yourself, 'In what way does Jesus, the bread of life, satisfy my hunger?'. John 6:25-35

11 'A branch cannot bear fruit by itself; it can only do so if it remains in the vine . . . Whoever remains in me, and I in him, will bear much fruit.' John 15:4, 5
Do we accept that, to achieve anything for Jesus, we need to be

totally dependent on him, like a branch on a tree, or do we try to do things in our own strength?

12 How can we make sure we 'remain in' Jesus (stay attached to, and dependent on, him)?

13 What sort of thing do you think Jesus meant when he talked about us 'bearing fruit'?

Who is Jesus?

How would you answer?

14 What would you say in reply to someone who said, 'I think Jesus was a good man, and a good moral teacher, but his disciples were deluded when they thought he was God.'?
(Note. Muslims claim that Jesus never said he was God, and that the Bible has been changed in this respect.)

15 How would you answer this argument?
'Anyone can claim to be God. It doesn't mean it's true.'
(Members of the Unification Church – 'Moonies' – claim that Jesus failed in his mission, and that Rev. Moon is the new Messiah.)

16 Why do you think people prefer to think of Jesus as simply 'a good man' or 'a good teacher', even though this doesn't make sense when we look at what he actually claimed?

17 Is it enough for us to say, 'Yes, I accept the fact that Jesus was the Son of God'? Is there more to being a Christian than just saying we believe it?

8 OPPOSITION

Why was Jesus arrested?

Read it for yourself
The accounts of Jesus' arrest and trial are in: Matthew 26:47 –
27:26; Mark 14:43 – 15:15; Luke 22:47 – 23:25; John 18:1 – 19:16

A quick check on the facts
1 You will find the answers to these questions in Mark 14 and
Luke 23:1-5.
 ● Who wanted Jesus arrested?
 ● Where did they plan to arrest him?
 ● Who helped them, and how?
 ● Did Jesus resist arrest?
 ● What happened when the Jewish authorities tried to get witnesses
to Jesus' 'crimes'?
 ● What charge did the Jewish (religious) authorities find him guilty
of?
 ● What was the penalty for this under Jewish law?
 ● What charges did they bring against Jesus when they took him to
the Roman (civil) authorities?
 ● Did Pilate find Jesus guilty?
 ● Why didn't he release Jesus?
 ● Whose release did the crowd ask for?

How is Jesus opposed today?

2 Do you think Christians in your own society face opposition today?
If you do, what forms do you think this opposition takes? If not,
why do you think there is little opposition?
3 'We fail to follow the Jesus who rocked the boat and put people's
backs up over the real abuses in society.' (*Jesus Then and Now*, page
121)
What do you think are the 'real abuses' in society today
 ● in your local community?
 ● in the wider world?
Do you think Christians say and do enough to oppose these wrongs
in society? Do you do anything about them?

The kingdom of God
4 'If one of you wants to be first, he must be the slave of all.'
Mark 10:44
Compare what Jesus said here with Matthew 5:38-42.
Does this mean we should let people 'walk all over us'?
Read James 2:1-9.

Prejudice in ourselves is really hard to detect, because we always seem to be able to find apparently good, logical reasons for our attitudes. Also, prejudice may remain hidden until something happens to bring it out into the open.

Ask yourself these questions:

5 Are there certain people, or groups of people, in my neighbourhood whom I try to avoid, so simply never bother to become involved with?

Why is this?

6 Does my local fellowship of Christians reflect the make-up of the neighbourhood: rich and poor, black and white, employed and unemployed, young and old? If not, why doesn't it? Does what we say or do, or how we do things as a fellowship suggest to the neighbourhood that church is only for certain types or classes of people?

7 'The world should look at us and see we are different. We are meant to be God's alternative society.' (*Jesus Then and Now,* page 125)

In an earlier section we looked at the difference there should be in the way we live as disciples. Do we feel that the people around us could look at our local fellowship and see something of God's pattern for an alternative society?

If not, what are we doing about it? Do we tend to blame everyone else in the church? Do we try to force our ideas on the rest of the fellowship? Do we look for another church? Or what can we do?

Feeling the pressure

8 Ridicule, apathy, or being given the cold shoulder because of our Christian faith very quickly wear down our patience and our love. This is especially so if we daily face a situation where we are the only Christian. How can we cope with this?

9 Think of the pressures that Martin Luther King and Oscar Romero, or Festo Kivengere, experienced. Is there anything we can learn for our own situation from how they responded? (See the video or pages 122, 125, 126 of the book.)

10 Whether or not you are in this sort of situation, try to think of another person in your group who may be, and remember to pray for him or her. There may be practical ways you can help – perhaps meeting such a person at lunchtime, to pray or just to have lunch and talk!

9 CRUCIFIXION

Why is the cross central to Christianity?

The cross as a symbol
1 What did a cross mean in the time of Jesus?
2 How do you think people view the cross as a symbol nowadays?
3 Why do people wear them?

Act it out
4 If someone is wearing a cross, there can be an opportunity to share the good news of Jesus with them. You may like to try a role-play with two people. One takes the role of a Christian and the other of someone who is not a Christian, but always wears a cross. Here is how a conversation might go:
    'Is that gold, that cross you're wearing?'
    'Yes, it's nice, isn't it? My boyfriend bought it for me.'
    'Why do you wear a cross? Do you think it means anything special?'
Discuss the conversation afterwards, and decide whether the 'Christian' was tactful or offensive, understandable or bewildering.
5 Read what Paul said about the cross in 1 Corinthians 1:17-25. Do you think people today are more likely to find the cross 'offensive' or simply 'nonsense'?
    Peter, who spent so much time with Jesus, was in no doubt as to what the cross meant:
'For Christ died for sins once and for all, a good man on behalf of sinners, in order to lead you to God.' 1 Peter 3:18

What is sin?

6 Many people today do not believe in 'absolute' right and wrong. They see everything as 'relative'. This means, in effect, that something may be 'good' in one situation and 'bad' in another. Christians believe that God has absolute standards of right and wrong, however hard they sometimes are to work out in practice. The Jews of Jesus' time would have accepted this completely. Usually, people only believe in absolute right and wrong if they also believe in the existence of God.
    How would you answer people who say:
'Who are you to say what's right and what's wrong?'
'I've never done anyone any harm.'
'God's just a killjoy. He doesn't want us to enjoy ourselves.'
'I can't help the way I am — I'm only human.'
These passages from the Bible may help you: Isaiah 59:1-4, 8-15; Romans 3:9-20

You could also look at Hosea 7:1, 2; Deuteronomy 7:7-11; 8:5, 6; Mark 2:7

7 We can easily deceive ourselves about what sin is, and its effect on us. Often we gloss over what is wrong with us, but are very good at seeing what's wrong with other people. Jesus pointed to this on many occasions.

Look at Luke 6:37-42. There is plenty of evidence for Jesus' sense of humour in this brief picture! If you have some creative minds in your group you may like to work out a brief dramatization of what Jesus said.

How is Jesus' death a solution to sin?

Read it for yourself
The story of the Passover is in Exodus 11:1 — 12:28. (You might like to replay David Watson's explanation of the first Passover on the video.)

8 Do you find the idea of sacrifice difficult to understand?

9 Try to think of examples where someone has sacrificed (given up) something for others.

10 Recently an old man who was unable to pay his rates was jailed — and then freed the following day because an anonymous well-wisher paid his fine for him. Is this an accurate picture of how Jesus' death is a solution for our sin? Read Romans 5:6-11 and see Paul explain how Jesus' death has solved our estrangement from God.

What did Jesus' death achieve?

11 Jesus saved us by his death on the cross. Have we experienced the meaning of this salvation in our own lives?

Look in turn at each of the pictures of what Jesus has done for us, and then think over how you have experienced being set free, put right, reconciled.

These verses may help to understand:
set free, bought back, redeemed — Ephesians 1:6-8;
Colossians 1:13, 14
put right, justified — Colossians 2:13, 14; Romans 4:25 and 5:1, 9
reconciled, made God's friends — 2 Corinthians 5:19, 20;
Colossians 1:21, 22

A thought for action
12 Jesus has reconciled us to God, and made us his friends. So have we tried, through our words and actions, to be reconciled to those who have something against us?

10 RESURRECTION

Is the resurrection important?

Read it for yourself
Matthew 27:57 – 28:15; Mark 15:42 – 16:8; Luke 23:50 – 24:49;
John 19:31 – 21:24

1 In *Jesus Then and Now,* the question is asked, 'Is the resurrection important?' What do you think?

Did Jesus really rise from death?

2 If someone challenges us to 'prove' the resurrection of Jesus, it can sometimes help to ask them about other things that they believe in, and why.

For example, try asking yourself – or someone else: Do you believe America exists? Do you believe deeply enough to get on a plane and go there?

Compare the reasons given with the reasons for believing in the resurrection, and look at the extent to which trust, or faith, leads to belief beyond reasonable doubt.

Is it hard to believe?
Read John 20:24-29

3 If you are working in a group, discuss honestly any aspect of the resurrection story which you find it hard to understand or accept. If you are using this book on your own, write down any queries you have and talk them over with another Christian, or read one of the books suggested at the end of this section.

Either Christianity is based on truth, or it is a lie. You can read what Paul said about this in 1 Corinthians 15:12-19.

4 One of the strongest pieces of evidence for the resurrection is the dramatic change in the disciples. See their state of mind before it happened: Mark 14:50 and 16:8; John 20:1, 2, 19 . . . and after: Acts 4:13-22 and 5:40-42.
Note the difference!
What difference does it make to our everyday lives that Jesus is alive?

5 Take one or two of the following statements, which might be made by someone not prepared to accept the resurrection, and decide how you would answer them.

● 'Jesus didn't actually die on the cross. He just passed out and then recovered in the tomb.'

● 'I think it was all wish-fulfilment. The disciples wanted to believe Jesus wasn't really dead, and so they had hallucinations about him being alive.'

- 'I reckon the disciples stole Jesus' body so that they could say he'd risen from the dead. That's what the authorities said at the time, isn't it? It's in the Bible.'
- 'The resurrection? Well, the disciples made a mistake, didn't they? They went to the wrong tomb, found it empty, and jumped to the conclusion that he'd come back to life.'
- 'Well, I think "intelligent" people don't really accept the physical resurrection of Jesus. I think the resurrection story is symbolic.'

6 If you're not sure how to answer some of these objections, replay the video sequence in the judge's chambers, or read through pages 145-155 of the book again. What other objections do people raise to believing in Jesus' resurrection?

What does the resurrection mean?

7 Look at some of the apostles' preaching in the early days of the church. What meaning did they see in the resurrection?
Read Acts 5:27-32; Acts 13:29-39

8 In *Jesus Then and Now*, David Watson and Simon Jenkins point to two things that the resurrection establishes (pages 156-57). What are they? Perhaps you can remember without turning back to the book? Here are two 'clues': What does 'vindicate' mean? Who, or what, has been defeated?

9 How docs the resurrection of Jesus affect our attitude to death?

For further discussion

10 Read 1 Corinthians 15:35-58. What question is asked, and how does Paul answer it?

If you want to read more about the evidence for the resurrection, these two books are excellent:
Who Moved the Stone? by Frank Morrison (Faber), described as 'the inner story of a man who originally set out to write one kind of book and found himself compelled by the sheer force of circumstances to write quite another'.
Verdict on the empty tomb, by Val Grieve (Falcon) — a lawyer looks at the facts.

11 THE SPIRIT

Read it for yourself
The ascension: Acts 1:3–11
The coming of the Spirit: Acts 2

A quick check on the facts
1 When, in relation to the resurrection, did the ascension happen?
2 What particular groups of people did Jesus appear to in this period?
3 What did Jesus do, and talk about, in the period between his resurrection and ascension?
4 What did he promise the disciples before he left them?

Can we believe in the ascension?

5 Do you find the ascension hard to believe or understand? If you do, discuss it with the group, or with another Christian.
6 What did the disciples believe had happened to Jesus?
Look at: Acts 2:33; 3:21; 5:31; 7:55, 56

Who is the Holy Spirit?

7 What was the work of the Spirit of God in Old Teastament times? (See page 162, *Jesus Then and Now*)
Here are some references to the work of the Spirit in the Old Testament: Genesis 1:2; Exodus 31:1-5; Numbers 11:23-29; 1 Chronicles 12:18; 2 Chronicles 15:1, 2; Psalm 104:30; Ezekiel 11:5
8 What did God promise to do in these two messages he gave to Ezekiel and Joel? Ezekiel 36:26, 27; Joel 2:28-32

Pictures of the Spirit in action
9 Imagine yourself in a situation where you long for:
● a breeze or wind;
● fire;
● water.
How are these situations like the work the Holy Spirit does in the life of a Christian? You might like to replay the video sequence at the watermill for a vivid picture of the Spirit in action.
10 Wind, fire and water are powerful forces and sometimes, in the physical world, we do not welcome their influence. As well as bringing comfort and refreshment, the Holy Spirit can be an uncomfortable influence in our lives. Can you think of examples where the Holy Spirit's work in your life could be (or has been) a disturbing experience?

How does the Spirit work?

11 What did Jesus tell his disciples about the work of the Holy Spirit?

Look at John 15:26; John 16:8, 13-15; Luke 12:11, 12.

12 See if you can find from these verses at least five ways in which the Spirit works.

Think for a few moments and then write down any particular areas of your life (personal or social) in which you feel you need the help of the Holy Spirit at the moment.

Next look at these verses and make a note of how the Spirit works in us: Romans 8:5, 15-17, 26, 27; Galatians 5:22, 23; 2 Corinthians 3:18

Now compare the two lists you have made, and spend some time thinking and praying over the way the Spirit can help.

(If you are watching the video, replay the part where Ian Petit speaks of cherries on a tree or bricks in water.)

What is the work of the Spirit?

13 Look at these two passages to see what is the Holy Spirit's work in the church (or fellowship of Christians): 1 Corinthians 12:4-7; Ephesians 4:2-7.

Do you think Christians today are guilty of neglecting either the gifts of the Spirit or the unity that the Spirit wishes to bring?

Filled with the Spirit

14 Imagine — or actually carry out — the following idea. (Doing it will make it stick in your mind much better!) Take a small glass or cup and fill it absolutely full to the brim with water. Carry it across the room and put it down. You'll find it very difficult not to spill any!

Now for what are probably the two easiest questions in this book! What is immediately noticeable, and why?

Sit down and re-read 'Filled with the Spirit', on page 174 of *Jesus Then and Now*. What can you learn from your action (carrying the full glass) about being filled with the Spirit? (Note. A lively alternative demonstration, which may produce other insights into the work of the Spirit, if you are working in a group, is to have a well-shaken bottle of lemonade handy.)

12 THE NEW AGE

Are Christians optimists or pessimists?

1 What are your feelings about:
   - your future?
   - the future of the world?
2 What are the things you fear most about the future?
3 Do you feel there is anything we can do to solve the world's problems?
4 Jesus said, 'Countries will fight each other; kingdoms will attack one another. There will be terrible earthquakes, famines and plagues everywhere; there will be strange and terrifying things coming from the sky.' Luke 21:10, 11. Does this mean that political changes, nuclear disarmament, ecology movements and so on are lost causes, and Christians should not waste time campaigning for them?
5 Christians run the risk of going to one of two extremes: either they deal with the world's problems and forget to preach the good news, or they are concerned with people's spiritual needs and forget that we all live in a real, physical world.

   Do you think this is true? Which extreme do you think you tend towards? From what you have learnt about Jesus, what do you think his attitude is?

How should we prepare for the future?

6 What do you think is the right attitude for Christians to take regarding the return of Jesus:
   - We should study the Bible so that we know when he will return?
   - We should live each day as if it were our last?
   - We should warn everyone that the end of the world is near?
   - We should seek to live as God wants us to live while we have time?
   - We should not take any precautions about the future because it may never arrive?
   - Or should we combine all of these?
   If you are working in a group, discuss these attitudes, and their strengths and weaknesses.
7 From looking at some of the following passages, what do you feel were the three main emphases in what Jesus said about his return? **Luke 21:27, 28; Matthew 25:1-13; Mark 13:26-37;** Matthew 7:21-23; Luke 19:11-27

How will God judge people?

8 How would you answer someone who said, 'How can a God of love punish people?'

Read again pages 183-87 in *Jesus Then and Now*. Do you agree with what the authors have written?

Heavy words about heaven and hell
Jesus spoke very clearly about the judgement of God and about hell as a place of separation from God and his love. Look at Luke 16:19-31; Matthew 18:8-14; Matthew 25:31-46

9 Why did Jesus talk about hell?
10 Why do we find the idea of hell so difficult?
11 What words did Jesus use to describe heaven?
Read Matthew 13:36-43

What is the Christian hope?

12 We have seen that Jesus talked about the kingdom of God as being here and now. And yet he talks of heaven as 'the kingdom' as well.
    Paul explained to some of the early Christians what it meant to be in the kingdom and yet waiting for the kingdom. You can read what he says: 2 Corinthians 1:21, 22; Ephesians 1:13, 14. Paul also shared how he felt about heaven, in 2 Corinthians 5:1-10.
    Do you ever feel as Paul did?
13 Many of us often have difficulty imagining what heaven will be like. Remember for a few moments some of the times in your life as a Christian when you have experienced God's love and power in a special way. That is a foretaste of what heaven is like! The Bible also gives us some pictures of heaven. Read Revelation 21:1-7; Revelation 21:22 – 22:5; Isaiah 2:4

Thought for action
14 Spend a few moments thinking of ways in which, through the way you live, you can bring the reality of heaven, God's kingdom, into the lives of the people around you each day.

For further reading
The Jesus Hope, Stephen Travis (IVP)
Hereafter, David Winter (Hodder)

NOTES

NOTES

NOTES

NOTES